PLANT SPIRIT MEDICINE

USING AN ANCIENT ANCESTRAL MEDITATION TO CONNECT WITH THE MEDICINE OF PLANTS

MICÁELA CORIA-CAREW ND LAC

LIVING
GRACE
Press

Living Grace Press

LivingGraceMeditation.com

4926 SE Woodstock Blvd PORTLAND, OR 97206

Email: livinggracemeditation@gmail.com

First edition. ISBNs as follows:

978-1-944627-00-3 - ebook

978-1-944627-01-0 - print

Cover Design and Meditation Drawings by

Asha McLaughlin, www.bloomwellness.info.

Logo artwork by Co Carew.

I dedicate this work to the benefit of all beings.

FOREWORD

A few years back, Mica and I were doing some bodywork training together, applying essential oils along a person's spine in a new, deliberate method called Aromatouch. As we worked with the second-to-last oil, Mica turned to me and said, "Aren't the waterfalls beautiful?"

"Huh?" I replied. I'd known Mica for years, but this was a new one.

"You know," she said, "the waterfalls that always happen after this particular oil. The blockages are starting to flow."

"Uh, no...I'm not seeing them."

"Really?" she replied, genuinely surprised.

Many times over the years, Mica has amazed me with her unique truths and insights into the world. One day we were making flight reservations together. I was going on about picking my seat on the side of the plane where I would best be able to see Mt. Hood as we approached Portland.

"Is that how you make your decisions, Josie?" she asked. "Hmmm, I see why you've been getting yourself into some troubles. You just need to go inside with the meditation and you will know the answer from your true wisdom rather than your mind. Everything flows when you make decisions from this place."

And, indeed, the flight went smoothly, and I had a beautiful view of the mountain without having to logistically figure it out. But bigger than this, I knew the smooth flow was the result of my ego/mind surrendering to a higher wisdom that I am now able to access within myself. This wisdom knows what is best for me, and not just me but all sentient beings, even with something as insignificant as an airline seat. Just imagine when we make bigger decisions from this place.

I come from white, Anglo-Saxon, Protestant heritage—the prevailing culture of the founding fathers of the United States and much of western civilization. Perhaps eons ago, my European ancestral culture contained the kind of wisdom revealed in this book. If so, our current cultural reality is such that much, or all, of that wisdom has been lost.

I met Dr. Micáela Coria-Carew ND, LAc, Apache Medicine Woman, on the first day of our medical school training over twenty years ago. Her astounding insights and wisdom on how to be fully embodied and spiritually connected have profoundly shifted how I live and walk in this world. This wisdom is timeless and she calls it Plant Spirit Medicine. have been privileged to bear witness to her journey of birthing her family's unspoken ancestral wisdom, knowledge, and healing out into the world and western culture.

The Plant Spirit Medicine she teaches in this book is of the most elemental wisdom. It returns us to our inner knowing. We learn and remember how to stay in Love and stay safe—within ourselves—no matter the external experience. It teaches us to navigate in a tumultuous world with grace and clear boundaries—boundaries that we begin to know and understand from our deepest places of wisdom.

The Plant Spirit Medicine meditation teaches us the middle path. The razor's edge between divine love and the discipline born of that divine love. It is from this meditation that we can begin to understand clear boundaries and how to stay safe in a warring universe, from the outer world to our inner consciousness.

The ancient wisdom Mica shares in this book, and the ability to practice it, is woefully lacking and forgotten in our current culture. This meditation is the medicine that has been called forth to help us heal ourselves.

Mica is giving voice to her people's ancient wisdom, their medicine, for us, so that we might begin to heal ourselves. What might the world look like if we accept this gift?

Josie Hannah Schmidt, ND

Portland, Oregon

August 2017

"The essence of what I have learned from Dr. Mica Carew and her lineage of teaching Plant Spirit Medicine is that existence is eager to communicate with you if you open your heart and simply ask and listen. Through a guided inquiry process that unites the breath with conscious intention, the plant world reveals its medicine effortlessly, poetically, and mystically. Plant Spirit Medicine empowered me to trust my own intuition and direct connection to nature. This work is permeated with the inner sensitivity of the conscious revelation of interdependence of all of life. How beautiful it is to be able to ask a plant "What is your medicine?" and receive the reply through circulating its essence through your own awareness.

"I highly recommend this body of work to anyone who is longing to awaken their connection to source. Freedom and deep love of life is at the core of this practice, so in its application my experience reflected back to me the essence of who I truly am. Thank you, thank you, thank you, Mica, for sharing this work with the awakening of beloveds who love the planet, this universe, as their own Self."

~ Bodhitara Searles

"Dr. Mica has been my physician, colleague, and dear friend for over fifteen years. She taught me the Plant Spirit Medicine meditation when I first began seeing her as a patient, and it was the first system of energy medicine that I could immediately sense in my body. It helped me through anxiety attacks after a bicycle accident and after a major anxiety attack when I found myself alone and stranded in China. This meditation practice has been a steady and helpful support for these last fifteen years. I've learned many other techniques of healing and meditation which are helpful, but this particular meditation is by far my foundation practice through which I evaluate, understand, and directly experience all others."

~ Julie Kaneshiro, MSOM, LAC

"I have done a lot of different meditations in my lifetime, and Mica's Plant Spirit Medicine meditation is unlike any other. It takes you deeply into the space where plants and humans communicate. This meditation is a gateway for natural healing, balance, and relaxation—physically, mentally, emotionally, and spiritually. I greatly recommend this book to everyone who is interested in benefiting from meditation."

~ Sandra Dawson

"What a treat to work with the Plant Spirit Meditation and deepen my understanding of these amazing medicines. With Mica's guidance, I feel I have a visceral, heart-based knowledge (instead of just my brain) of the way the plants are here to help. I recommend Plant Spirit Medicine for anyone ready to open themselves to a more personal and intimate connection with the medicine inherent in plants. I use the insights I have gained every day in my practice working with patients."

~ Louise Rose, ND

Rose Cabinet Medicine

"Mica is a divine conduit, and spirit flows clearly through her profound understanding and guidance of Plant Spirit Medicine. The meditation takes you deep, as it taps into the vast wisdom of the known and unknown. It is a divine gift for everyone who journeys within."

~ Aisha Harley

Native American Ceremony Prayer

I clear my mind so that I may have good thoughts
for myself and others.
I clear my ears so I may appreciate mother earth's sweet sounds.
I clear my eyes so I may see the beauty in myself and others.
I clear my nose so I may take in and appreciate
mother earth's beautiful fragrances.
I clear my lips so I may speak well about myself and others.
I clear my heart so I may honor the true nature
in myself and others.
I clear my body so I may treat my body
and other bodies respectfully.
I clear my feet so I may be reminded to walk reverently
and gently on mother earth.

***Plant Spirit Medicine* –**

"Hush, Mija. It's time to be quiet now."

"I'm not talking, Gammy."

"Yes, it's time to quiet your mind so you can listen to the rhythm of the earth."

INTRODUCTION

What you will be learning here are universal truths which I have learned through my ancestral heritage as an Apache Medicine Woman. You may recognize some of these techniques and insights from other modalities. When I started studying the eastern traditions I felt relief in knowing other cultures had not lost this ancient wisdom. I knew then that my family and I did not have to keep this a secret anymore, because other cultures were teaching aspects of it. But what I experienced in other cultures was the setting up of the framework for accessing spiritual knowledge. Never have I experienced the Plant Spirit Medicine meditation in its entirety, as my grandmother taught me. So while parts are universal, the whole meditation is specific to my heritage. It is only through this meditation that I have been able to access the deep levels of wisdom and healing that plants are so willing to provide. The women in my family have been passing down this information for generations, and now I am sharing it with you.

Throughout history, Apaches have been known to be a mystical ethnic group, possessing special medicinal and clairvoyant skills. I come from that Apache lineage, from an unbroken line of Medicine Women.

Through all the changes and discrimination my family has experienced my grandmother ensured that we kept this knowledge intact. When my grandmother was nine, she became a victim of human trafficking. Her mom and siblings owed a debt to the shopkeeper for $13.50. Because they could not pay this, the shopkeeper took my grandmother in exchange to pay off the debt. Grandma used this meditation over the years to survive her ordeal and eventually escape to safety with the four children she had by the time she was fourteen.

Grandma didn't just have this meditation as a concept, she lived it. There was no separation from this place of knowing. It was just what she was, and it was her compass.

When I was a young girl, Grandma taught me this practice from my native lineage. When I close my eyes and think, feel, and sense what Plant Spirit Medicine is for me, the words that come up are gratitude, reverence, heart exchange, and deep, deep healing. The Plant Spirit Medicine Meditation has not been broken. It has been carried forward intact from one generation to the next.

I am honored to share this sacred meditation with my fellow Plant Spirit Medicine family. If you are holding this book then that means you, and this book is in appreciation of you, with great gratitude and reverence. This is my heart exchange with you. I want you to know this medicine now. My family wants you to know this medicine now. It is the time for all of us to do deep, deep healing. Thank you for being called to love the plants and to love mother earth and care for her.

As you read these pages, know that the medicine is "doing you." Trust it even if you do not see, sense, or feel it happening. No matter where you are in your life, no matter what ups or downs you are going through, this is a gift to you. Know that this is sacred medicine, because these plant essences are from the divine. They are an expression of the divine. They are here to heal us in body, mind, and spirit.

You may have heard that a specific essential oil or medicinal herb or plant is good for a certain condition of either the body, mind, or spirit. That's all fine, and please do any research you like, but also remember that in the meditation you bypass any preconceived idea of what the plant or essential oils are supposed to do. You journey to a deeper level, where you access your inner knowing and true consciousness. These will connect with the medicine of the plants on a deeper level than your brain will. When you take in the fragrance of the essential oil, feel what it's doing in your body. Realize you are having a direct experience with the plant or essential oil. You are creating your own relationship with it, and it will support you in ways specific to you. Just let the plant essence do the work it knows to do.

When we do Plant Spirit Medicine together, we are connecting to the divine within us. We are connecting to the divine in each other. We create more love and compassion for each other, because Plant Spirit Medicine is like a prayer. With prayer, truth and love become heightened and alive. The mind chatter and all the doubts, the monkey mind, dissolve and more god can be heard. It takes you back to where "normal" should be.

I

GRANDMA'S GARDEN

1

GRANDMA'S GARDEN –

There are so many reasons for developing a relationship with the plants and the trees and nature. One of the biggest is to develop a better understanding and respect for what nature is doing for you, especially how it can heal you physically, mentally/emotionally, and spiritually. Also, when you develop a relationship with a plant (or anything else), you are less likely to want to destroy it. Instead, you are more likely to want to treat it with respect, especially when you see what it's giving to you.

Grandma always had a garden of some sort. Even when she lived next to the railroad tracks. The one I remember the most looked like a small, gravelly square near the back of the house.

She would say, "Whatever it takes, a space near where you live is calling to be made into a garden."

She would often do her healing work for trade, and receive in return vegetables, garlic, cilantro, onions, and medicinal herbs. What she always grew in her own garden were pinto beans, corn, and squash. She called them the "three sisters." These three planted together are sacred, she would say. "It's the medicine between the three of them that allow them to grow strong and healthy. And then you will grow strong and healthy." She planted the three sisters close together, and we now know that growing these three things together was a widespread practice among the indigenous people throughout the Americas. What happens is the bean vine grows around the corn stalk, fixing the nitrogen to the soil, while the squash provides a shady ground cover that locks in moisture and keeps weeds and insects at bay.

I wasn't allowed to go out with her when she did the planting, but watched from the house window. Really, you would think that nothing could grow in that gravel patch. But sure enough, every year she would have beans, corn, and squash. She would sit there on her knees planting and it looked as though she was feeling the rhythm of the earth, feeling the wind, and just being with that gravel. She treated it with such respect and honor, making a connection with it. This was her offering, this was her prayer. She was doing the meditation in her body and connecting her heart with the space around her—thanking it, expressing gratitude for it. Letting it know that she would soon be planting the sacred three sisters.

Watching her preparing to plant reminded me of how she would bathe too, giving deep, deep gratitude to the warm water. Her intention in the bath water was potent and poignant and intentful, and this was the same feeling when she was planting. She was so clear and full of intent. It was as if she were making a new friend, and all her focus was on that friend, except in this case her friend was her soon-to-be garden—the land that would help cultivate her sacred three sisters. She most always invited me in to join her in whatever she did, but this was one thing that was just for her. Now, I see why. She was developing a deep relationship with the land and the soon-to-be garden.

The sacred three sisters provided food for many people who came by unannounced. She also never turned away any of the people who jumped the trains. At that time, many people were looking for work and jumped the trains to travel. When they came to the back door she always offered them food, and she built a reputation as a house that would feed you if you were hungry and in need.

Every year her garden was plentiful with pinto beans, corn, and squash. I believe that part of why her garden was so plentiful was because of the preparation ceremony she had before she planted anything. It was such a conscious, deliberate action, and she was respectful doing her meditation. She then planted when it was time.

Your Own Garden

1. If you think you need to have a lot of space to have a garden: YOU DON'T. A little space will do. If you have no yard, plant in a small pot. I used to plant my pinto beans in a paper cup and a moist napkin.

2. Develop a relationship with the land where you live.

3. Find some seeds that you are attracted to. It could be flower seeds or veggies of any sort.

4. Sit like Grandma did with your area that you are going to plant in or your pot and soil.

5. Feel the space around you. Place your hands on your heart and say, "Thank you, space."

6. Relax your face and drop your jaw. Place your tongue on the bottom of your mouth with the tip on the gum line of the bottom of the teeth. Breathe into home base safe place, the space below your bellybutton.

Visualize the color yellow there and say, "Hello, land" or "Hello, soil and pot." "Thank you so much for being here with me."

7. Bathe your tail bone with the white glistening light, and then visualize that light going all the way down to mother earth. "Thank you, divine mother earth, for providing me with the soil I am planting with today." All the while, breathe into the yellow glow in the space below your belly button.

8. Direct your attention fully to this home base safe place.

9. Visualize a beautiful, glistening white light coming out of the top of your head as you connect to the divine quality of gratitude. "Thank you for my body and how it can connect to the soil and to the natural world. I am so grateful."

10. Back to home base safe place. "Thank you, earth, thank you, seeds." Now say thanks to the seeds that you specifically planted.

11. Bathe your heart with a light pink waterfall or glow. "I connect my divine heart energy to the seeds and the soil and the water that will help this garden grow. Thank you for providing me with beauty and sustenance."

12. Breathe in and out, in and out. Visualize your heart energy pouring onto the seeds and the soil. Visualize a glow of bright light coming from the soil and the seeds coming up to meet you at your heart.

13. Stay focused like Grandma was. Keep doing this until you feel like there is a space, a window. (If you don't know what this feels like, it's okay. Just pretend that you do and eventually you will be able to.) Now place your hands on the soil and start moving or kneading it. "Thank you for this opportunity to plant you today. I am so grateful."

14. Plant your seeds and water them. "Thank you, water, for your sustenance for me and for these seeds. I am so grateful." All the while, you are bathing your heart and connecting with the water, soil, and seeds.

CONNECTING WITH ANY GARDEN OR PLANT

Maybe you are not going to be planting but would just like to connect with a plant that you already have or your garden.

1. Sit with your garden or plant.

2. Drop your jaw and place the tip of your tongue at the base of your bottom teeth. Go to the home base safe place.

3. Your plant is in front of you or you are sitting in your garden. Breathe into the space below your belly button and start your practice of the divine quality of gratitude as we did above.

4. Visualize your breath traveling down to your home base safe place. Place your hands on your heart and say, "Thank you, garden. Thank you, plant. I am so happy and grateful you are in my life."

5. Connect with the divine white light at your tail bone, and then bring that light down to the core of divine mother earth. "Thank you, mother earth, for providing such beauty for me and providing me with sustenance. I am so grateful."

6. Back to home base safe place. Visualize a beautiful shimmery light going from the top of your head to the divine quality of gratitude.

7. Then home base safe place.

8. Bathe your heart with a light pink glow to wake up the heart energy. Visualize your beautiful heart energy beaming out and showering over the plant or garden. You can place your hands on your heart to help you

activate your heart energy and to help you visualize your heart energy beaming out. Visualize the plant or the garden having a beautiful white shimmery glow coming from it and beaming out at you. "Thank you, plant/garden, for connecting with me."

YOU WILL BE AMAZED AT HOW YOUR RELATIONSHIP WITH YOUR GARDEN OR the plant will change and develop. Give it a try. When I give a plant or my garden that much focus, I never look at it the same. Or I should say I REALLY look at it.

3

Hiking or Jogging

This practice doesn't even have to be done with a garden or plant. I do it while I'm hiking. I may be walking along and a tree or bush or something just stops me. Well…I do want to keep hiking so I'm not going to take too much time and hold up the group, but when something catches my eye, I pay attention. I stop, then I go to face relaxation and home base safe place, etc.

I bathe my heart with the pink, and I say, "Hello beautiful _____, (tree, shrub, bush, etc.). Thank you so much. I am so grateful to you. Thank you for your beauty and for creating oxygen." I visualize the plant glowing. I pour out my pink heart glow, and we connect via glows. Then I move on.

I also do this when I'm jogging. I will be breathing into the space below my belly button while I'm jogging, then I bathe my heart and flow some kind of divine quality. I practice bringing the divine quality of gratitude for my surroundings and for my body, all while I'm jogging along.

4

The Meditation as a Way of Life

While what you're learning here is the Plant Spirit Medicine meditation, incorporating the divine essence of a particular plant, my grandmother used the foundation of the meditation for all aspects of her life, including healing people. The foundational meditation is simply all the steps of the Plant Spirit Medicine meditation without using a specific plant. My grandmother performed her healing work by first quieting her mind with this meditation. Over time it was so automatic that it was just her form of being. She was the meditation. When a sick person came for a treatment, she would also consciously do this entire meditation, and the energy in the room immediately changed. It felt like a sacred temple, because she had become a sacred temple and the surroundings were a sacred temple. She called in the divine healing energy to flow over her and through her and in the process became a beautiful chalice, filled with the divine love and grace of healing medicine.

As she healed people, I followed along doing my meditation as I was taught. I did it step by step, just as I have outlined here for you. It hasn't changed. It is exactly what Grandma did and what she taught me. The only difference is that Grandma had more practice so she could do it faster. Now that I am older and have had more practice I do it at what call "Grandma pace."

While within the meditation, Grandma would sit quietly and feel the rhythms of the body of the person she wanted to heal. She could feel when the person's rhythm was off or out of synch. From there she would do bodywork and offer the person herbal medicine. She knew what herbal medicine to use because she had developed a relationship with the plants and herbs. She meditated with each plant individually just as I am showing you how to do in this book. The herb she needed for someone would appear in her mind's eye. The Plant Spirit Medicine would appear to help her and the person. It came easily and effortlessly to her because of the many times she had sat with the plant and developed her relationship with that particular plant through this meditation.

Now you can do this too. It is simple, precise, and thorough. This is all you need if you want to speak to the plant spirits.

BEFORE WE GET STARTED WE NEED TO TALK ABOUT ESSENTIAL OILS

I want to be very clear that I care about your safety, and therefore the essential oils you use are important to me. Not all essential oils on the market are equally pure, and I could not in good conscience go further without talking about the importance of this purity. Quality really does matter.

The first thing to understand is the sourcing of the plant used for the oil. When I was training in my Masters of Chinese Medicine program at the National University of Natural Medicine, the Chinese medicine doctors made it very clear that the soil and origin of where the herbs grew affected the outcome when using the herbs for clinical purposes. We learned that there was an art to growing and harvesting the herbs. For example, it was important to plant a medicinal herb at a certain time of year specific to that herb. The herb also needed to be harvested at a certain time of year, whether during a moon phase or just before the break of dawn. Families that have been carrying on this tradition are experts in their field and should be the ones growing and harvesting plants for the essential oils. Just as this meditation is from a long lineage, so should be the growers and harvesters of the plants and flowers that you will use.

It is also important for the supplier of the essential oils to have a trusted partnership with the growers/harvesters and distillers. And it's critical that the supplier always pays a fair price for their labor.

I use the essential oils from one company only, because I have found these oils to be pristine. Please remember that when the oil is pristine and unadulterated, the information of the plant is much more accessible. You want to be certain that the only components in the oil are those of the plant. Connecting and communicating with the spirit of the plant is much easier when there isn't a lot of static or rubbish to get through. Also, I don't want to connect and communicate with something that isn't pristine and of the highest divine frequency of the plant spirit world.

I also use oils from this specific supplier because they are respectful in their cultivation practices. They respect the growers and the harvesters and they give back to the communities they work with.

When you use any essential oils, please be aware of the interconnectedness of all things. Every part of this practice needs to be pristine, all the way from the growers to the company to the final product. This is the best and most appropriate way to respect mother earth. If one part of the whole is missing, then it's not worth using the essential oil. You want your oils to be pure, physically and energetically. You want the supplier to have what I call "right livelihood." This means the supplier of the essential oils is able to affect all those involved in a positive way —from the earth, plant, growers, harvesters, and distillers to the sellers. Full circle positive.

To begin your journey with the Plant spirits and to purchase my preferred essential oils, visit my website: <u>My.doterra.com/drmica</u>.

II

THE PLANT SPIRIT MEDICINE MEDITATION

5

THE PLANT SPIRIT MEDICINE MEDITATION

For this example, I'll use the plant spirit in its essential oil form of lemon. I like to use essential oils, because they are accessible to many of the people who have studied Plant Spirit Medicine with me. Also, if people use the same essential oil from the same supplier, I can have some guarantee that the oil will be consistent.

Many varieties of oils are available for us (for example, we could use lavender, wild orange, neroli, jasmine, clary sage, etc.). If we use oils from the same supplier, I can be certain that we are all using the same type of plant from the same region and soil. I like the consistency for group purposes, so we all can receive information from the plant spirit from its place of origin.

In the meditation, most of the time I use the oil internally, topically, and aromatically. I place a drop on my tongue, and rub some on my palms which I then place over my nose and breathe in, and I diffuse it as well. Diffusing an oil is when you place it in what's called a diffuser, which causes the oil to vaporize into the air. Sometimes I place a few drops in the hot water I drink. I like to use the essential oil physically so I am sure to get as much information from the plant spirit as I can. I also want it to heal me in ways I don't even know need to be healed. Using the essential oil physically helps that process along, and I am able to receive the most benefit out of my meditation. I can heal on all levels.

Because I use most of the oils internally, I cannot stress the importance of choosing essential oils from a company that allows no adulteration of the oil. Please research your essential oil company thoroughly, and also read the label on the bottle. Look for a "Supplement Facts" label so you can see exactly what's in the oil. If the bottle does not have a Supplement Facts label on it, don't ingest the oil. Some of the oils from the company I use do not have this label and I know not to ingest the oil. In the beginning, some people are uncomfortable placing even a small amount of oil on the tongue. If you are uncertain, please don't do it. Remember, I also diffuse the oil into the air and rub it on the palms of my hands which I then place over my nose and breathe it in.

I have provided you with all the tools you need to do the meditation on your own, including the written instructions and illustrations that follow. I have also provided guided audio recordings (available on my website Livinggracemeditation.com).

LET'S GET STARTED.

6

SETTLING INTO YOUR SPACE –

First, settle into your space. Find a comfortable place to sit or lie down, either in your home or outside with nature. Just make sure you will be free from distractions for the next twenty minutes. Take out the essential oil that you will be using for the meditation and place some drops on your tongue, rub onto your palms and breathe in, and/or use in your diffuser. Keep your oil near as periodically you will reapply it.

7

NEXT, TO YOUR OWN COUNT OF TEN, CALL YOUR SPIRIT INTO YOUR BODY.

Invite your angels and guides in. If you don't have any specific ones, then simply invite the one that you pray to or the divine universe, whatever works for you. Offer your angels and guides or whoever you pray to a gift. Maybe it's the dawn light, or the gentle breeze on your cheek, or the smile of your child. Do this with deep gratitude. Place your hands over your heart and think of three things you are grateful for. Doing just this helps to increase your vibration and your ability to connect to the plant spirit world.

Finally, state your intention to connect deeply and with gratitude to the oil and the Plant Spirit Medicine. You may also choose a divine quality to work with, such as kindness or patience.

8

Home Base Safe Place –

Feel your body touching the floor, pillow, or chair. Maybe you are lying down. Just feel your body connecting with whatever you are sitting or lying on.

Drop your jaw. Place the tip of your tongue on the gum line at the base of your bottom teeth.

Breathe into the yellow space below your belly button. This is your home base safe place. You can place your hand here to help you connect. If you can't see the yellow space, that's okay. Just breathe there anyway and know it's all happening.

With every breath set your intention for this particular meditation. I say, "Thank you so much, lemon essential oil, and to the spirit of the lemon. Thank you to the plant spirit world for your medicine and for all that you have to offer. I am so grateful." You always want to express gratitude and thanks. By setting your intention in this way, you set the stage for the best outcome of your meditation practice.

From this point, say, "I am preparing myself to communicate, if I have permission from the plant spirit world, and to specifically learn from the spirit of lemon." The words don't have to be exact, but always use gratitude with your intention.

Breathe into the space below your bellybutton. Visualize the color yellow there. The yellow in the space below your bellybutton is your "home base safe place." Now call in the divine essence of lemon essential oil to fill up the space below your belly button. Just breathe. Let it happen. We will get closer and closer and more intimate with the plant spirit of lemon as the meditation continues. Please do not force this process. It's like you are developing a new friendship. "Thank you, lemon."

As the lemon energy courses through your lower belly it is healing you on all levels: physical, mental/emotional, and spiritual. It will heal you in ways specific to you.

9

SETTING THE EARTHLY POLE –

Go back to the feeling of your body touching the floor or chair. Bring your attention to where they connect. Visualize a beautiful, glistening white light at your tailbone. As you visualize the white shimmery light or glow, ask for the divine spirit of lemon to go there. Ask it to wash over that area. Bathe the area with the plant spirit of lemon. You may feel sensations in your body. Just writing this process with you at this moment I am experiencing it.

Visualize that beautiful stream of light streaming down, down, down to the core of divine mother earth. You are setting the earthly pole. If you can't see or sense this, just pretend that you can, and eventually you will be able to. The divine essence of lemon is connecting to your tailbone, and you are bringing this divine essence all the way down to the core of divine mother earth. Take your time here. Experience the white light and your connection to mother earth.

"Thank you, lemon essential oil." I say this intermittently throughout the meditation. It is just something I feel to say, because I am trul grateful to be able to have this deep connection with the plant world. realize this is an honor and not everyone knows how to communicat with the plant world.

10

Back to Home Base Safe Place –

Gently make your way back to home base safe place. Place a few drops of your essential oil on your palms and breathe it in. Again, ask that the divine essence of the lemon essential oil (or you can say the plant spirit of the lemon) circulates in the space below your belly button. Let it heal your body in any way it needs to be healed. Now you are becoming more and more intimate with the spirit of the plant.

The relationship you have with any plant you do this with will never be the same. Each time I do the Plant Spirit Medicine with a new plant it truly is like getting to know a person and their personality. It's not a stranger anymore, because you are still circulating the plant. I journey with the plant spirits one at a time in the essential oil form, and I also journey with the essential oil blends. When multiple plant extracts are put together, they create their own special plant spirit essence. I am always saying thank you in great heartfelt gratitude. "Thank you so much for healing me; thank you so much for sharing your wisdom with me."

11

SETTING THE HEAVENLY POLE –

Gently make your way up to the top of your head. Remember, your jaw is dropped and your tongue is on the bottom of the mouth. The tip of the tongue is on the gum line at the base of the bottom teeth.

Now visualize a beautiful stream of light coming from the top of your head all the way up into the divine heavens. Set your intention by saying, "I am connecting to the divine plant spirit of lemon." Once again, it's okay if you cannot see, sense, or feel anything, just pretend that you can. Eventually you will be able to. It is happening whether you know it or not. Take your time here with this divine connection.

BACK TO HOME BASE SAFE PLACE –

Gently make your way back to home base safe place. Place a couple drops of lemon essential oil on your palms and breathe it in. Circulate the divine essence of lemon in the space below your belly button.

"Thank you, lemon."

OPENING YOUR HEART CONSCIOUSNESS –

Raise your shoulders up to your ears and rotate them back and down, opening up your chest cavity. In the upper part of the back, imagine a light pink waterfall or light pink glow. You are waking up the heart so it will connect and communicate with the divine plant spirit. Take your time here. Ask lemon's divine spirit to bathe the upper part of your back. You can use the light pink waterfall to help the divine essence of the plant intermingle with your heart.

"Thank you, divine plant spirit."

This is also a good point to breathe in more lemon, or drink some, or place a small amount of lemon essential oil on the tip of your tongue.

Now, gently make your way up to the front of your chest. Bathe the upper part of your chest with the light pink waterfall. Call in the divine essence of the plant spirit and ask it to intermingle with your heart. Remember that all along it is helping to heal your heart, your physical body, and all your energy bodies.

"Thank you, plant spirit."

You are learning about the plant spirit, and you may begin to receive information about it. It's okay if you don't. Often, you will get light bulb moments over time regarding the plant you worked with. It may be immediately or days, weeks, or months. You may get pictures, or someone you run into may need that oil for something and you happen to have it. Know that the divine plant spirits want to communicate with us. They are here for us.

BACK TO HOME BASE SAFE PLACE –

Gently go back to home base safe place. Place a couple of drops of lemon oil on your palms and breathe it in. Circulate the divine essence of the plant in the space below your belly button.

SETTING THE FLOWER BUD AT THE TOP OF YOUR HEAD –

Go to the top of your head and visualize a beautiful flower bud the size of prayer hands.

Remember that you don't have to keep setting your earthly or heavenly poles. Once you have established them, they stay there with you.

BLOSSOMING FLOWER –

Breathing into the space below your belly button, allow the flower to blossom on its own. Call in the divine essence of lemon. Visualize the divine essence of lemon flowing down through the center of the blossomed flower. It's like a dewy nectar that is flowing through the flower blossom. Let it circulate down through the center of your body and down to the core of divine mother earth. As it flows down, it is healing every cell in your body. You don't have to concentrate on it. Because it has been activated, it will continue to flow through you, so just allow it to happen. Picture this at least three times before you move on. It is so beautiful.

"Thank you, lemon."

1 7

FLOWER FULLY OPEN –

The flower is now fully open. Allow the divine spirit of lemon to course through your body.

"Thank you, lemon."

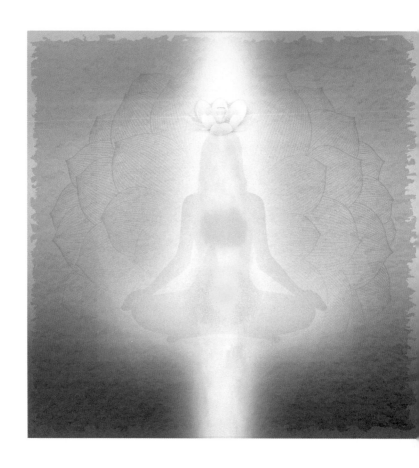

DIVINE WHITE LIGHT –

Visualize the divine essence of the plant flowing through your body and over your body. It's as if you are under a beautiful waterfall of the divine essence of the plant. It's moving through you and over you.

"Thank you, lemon. Thank you so much for sharing your wisdom and your guidance and for healing me specifically for my body. Thank you. In such gratitude."

Hands to heart center. Then place them down at the space below your belly button. Bow to your sacred heart. Then bow and thank the divine plant spirit you have worked with.

"Thank you for sharing your beautiful plant spirit with me."

WHAT TO EXPECT

When you do this meditation as a daily practice, eventually you will be able to tune in to all the subtle energies around you, not just the divine energies of the plants, essential oils, or medicinal herbs. You will be able to further feel the rhythm and the heartbeat of the earth. You will be able to hear the messages of the earth. With time and practice, you may be able to understand the medicine of the wind, to feel its energy and whispers. You may be able to access and connect with more of your true nature, and listen and trust what your inner knowing is telling you. These messages will be specific to you and your family to help heal and support you all.

Your senses for understanding the subtle energies of the earth will be more understood, heightened. And then you can be an instrument in helping to heal the planet. This is what I call living in grace.

With Gratitude

We are inviting you to use this information with reverence. It is with gratitude that my family offers you this ancient wisdom.

"Three Sisters." From left to right: Beautiful Woman Guided by Wisdom, Gentle Healer Walks in Beauty, Shining Star. August 2017.

Grandma Coria and myself. 1990.

Grandma Coria and my mother, Ruth Carew.

ACKNOWLEDGMENTS

I would like to acknowledge my grandmother, Margarita Coria, for keeping this "sacred medicine intact and alive."

Thank you.

I have so much love and gratitude to all my relations: my father William L. Carew, my mom Ruth (Refugio) Carew, my sisters Colleen Mary Carew (Beautiful Woman Guided by Wisdom) and Cynthia Marie Carew (Shining Star), and my brother who is with us in spirit, the late William Scott Carew. My husband William Wan and my daughter Sasha Wan Carew (Bright Eyes Smiling). William Starkey, Mesa Starkey (Blue Jay Calling 4 Directions), Aja Starkey (Dancing Dove). Our aunties: the late Auntie Irene, the late Auntie Senovia, the late Auntie Alice, and the late Rubin Coria. Roxanne Meding and family, Philip and Greg Mancera and family, Rochelle Sanchez and family, Roseanne Salinas and family. You all have always been there to support and love me and to take care of grandma Margarita Coria. Words cannot describe the depth of love I have for each and every one of you.

I want to thank my teachers at NUNM: the late Dr. Mengke Kou, LAc, who is with me in spirit now; Dr. Jared Zeff, ND, LAc and Lauren Zeff, Dr. Satya Ambrose, ND, LAc; Dr. Steven Sandberg-Lewis, ND, DHANP; Dr. Heiner Frehauf, PhD, LAc and Sharon Frehauf. These are the teachers (medicine people) who recognized me as a fellow medicine person early on in my naturopathic school training. They pushed me to not hide what I knew but to use what I was learning in naturopathic and Chinese medicine to fine tune my medicine.

I would like to acknowledge my wonderful friends: Hillary Larson, Dr. Nichole Lang, MD, Julie Kaneshiro, LAc, and family, Dr. Josie Schmidt, ND, Dr. Sundara Delphini, ND, LAc, Tawnya Fox and Jennifer Braine, Shawn Soszka and family, Alex McBride, Aisha Harley and Ariana Harley, Carole Downing, Dr. Jacqui Villalobos, ND, Dr. Rebecca Reese, MD, Paul Maeding and family, Rachel Gross and family, Dr. Jenny Tufenkian ND and family, my parent's church friends that take such good care of them, and our entire dōTERRA team. A special thank you to Asha McLaughlin for her beautiful artwork within the book and on the cover.

I would like to thank my spiritual teachers: Yangsi Rinpoche, President of Maitripa College, and Gangaji. Two very different spiritual teachers having the same message. I call them my book ends. They have kept me steady on my spiritual practice because they are so committed to their own practice of listening to the truth of their heart. Thank you.

Thank you, Creator, for my editor Karen Lacey. I was praying for just the right person to show up who would have the expertise and openness to take this project on; to help me express in words what has never been written. To help me take an understanding of "being" which is what I live daily and help me express that into the written word. Amazing!

Thank you to the company dōTERRA for caring so much and working so hard to make pristine essential oils accessible to so many. This is truly medicine for the people. Thank you for understanding the deep, deep healing that the plants and their essential oils have. Lastly, thank you dōTERRA for honoring the earth and using diligence with your gathering practices. I am overwhelmed with gratitude when I think of the Co-impact Sourcing initiative and the Healing Hands Foundation™. A percentage of the proceeds from the sale of this book will be donated to dōTERRA's Healing Hands Foundation™ partnership with Operation Underground Railroad (OUR Rescue). OUR Rescue's mission is to physically rescue children enslaved in sex trafficking.

Finally, to my Qi Gong group. They are a dedicated group of women who have been learning this medicine from me every Wednesday since 1998. Your dedication for showing up is inspiring. You have pushed me to write this book. Thank you for your patience.

FINALLY

I come from a lineage that shares information through the oral tradition and also through what is called transmission. Transmission is when one person, in this case my grandmother, knew something so well—she knew it in every cell of her body—that when you were with her you would receive the teaching, the lesson, the information without using the spoken word. Writing this *Plant Spirit Medicine* book was something I was guided to take action on. My true strength is teaching verbally. Because of this, I have recorded myself talking you through the Plant Spirit Medicine meditation using several oils. These meditations correlate with the oils listed in the back of the book. Please go to the website livinggracemeditation.com to listen and utilize the recorded meditations I have created for you.

It's important to write down what you receive when you are doing the meditation, and I have left pages at the end of this book for you to begin your Plant Spirit Medicine journey. Memories, thoughts, and ideas may pop up. Do not analyze them; just write them down. After doing the Plant Spirit Medicine meditation, your relationship with that plant will continue. The meditation is just the beginning. The plant and its wisdom and healing powers are now in your cells. It's doing you. Carry this book with you and write in it freely. You will get ideas in unexpected moments. Know that the plant spirits are working with you and communicating with you now. It's as if you have taken off the cobwebs from a door that was always there for you.

Please also go my website to learn more about how to take ongoing classes and workshops with more of the Plant Spirit Medicines via the essential oils. To purchase my preferred essential oils, visit this site directly: My.doterra.-com/drmica. We would love to have you journey with us.

I dedicate the finishing of this Plant Spirit Medicine book for the benefit of mother earth and all beings.

III

LISTEN TO THE MEDICINE OF THE PLANTS

Lemon

Peppermint

Wild Orange

clary Sage

Lavender

Frankincense

Neroli

Jasmine

Birch

Blue Tansy

Copaiba

Rose

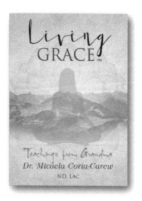

Teachings From Grandma: Living Life As Grace

Storytelling is powerful medicine in the native culture. See how it is used in
the most exquisite way as this book takes you on a journey through the lives of
ordinary people. This is a collection of personal stories that reflect what is
possible when grace is invited into everyday life.

———

*To find Plant Spirit Medicine recordings, workshops or for more information on
essential oils go to Livinggracemeditation.com.*

Made in the USA
Coppell, TX
23 March 2020

17559082R00067